Why Worry?

Why Worry?
Conquering a Common Inclination

James R. Beck
and David T. Moore

Baker Books

A Division of Baker Book House Co
Grand Rapids, Michigan 49516

©1994 by James R. Beck and David T. Moore

Published by Baker Books,
a division of Baker Book House Company
P.O. Box 6287
Grand Rapids, Michigan 49516-6287

Printed in the United States of America

Library of Congress Cataloging-in-Publication Data
Beck, James R.
    Why worry? : conquering a common inclination / James R. Beck
and David T. Moore.
        p. cm. —(Strategic Christian living)
      ISBN 0-8010-1092-6
      1. Worry—Religious aspects—Christianity. 2. Christian life.
    I. Moore, David T. II. Title. III. Series.
BV4908.5.B43   1994
248.8'6—dc20
                                          94-20699

Contents

How to Use This Book   7

1 Don't Worry about It   9

2 The Agony of Worry   25

3 Worrying about Worry   41

4 Acting on Worry   57

5 The Last Word on Worry   73

How to Use This Book

W e have written this book with worriers in mind. Worriers, and we authors include ourselves in this class, are predictable. Worriers like to have all the facts, they like to anticipate their options thoroughly, and they want a no-nonsense approach to issues. So we have designed this workbook with those features: a complete review of worriers and how they tick, a host of strategies worriers can implement to move into the peace and joy God wishes them to enjoy, and a practical tone to the whole book.

Worriers cannot snap their fingers to rid themselves of long-standing worry patterns. Habitual worry can grip our lives. If we do not diligently work to contain the deadly habit, worry can eventually choke out all the joy of living. But we have good news: worry is containable. Worry will give way to joy and peace if we follow God's prescriptions. Worriers can find freedom from their constant dread of the future.

How can worriers find this freedom? By developing new attitudes and perspectives on the future. The Bible speaks directly to the worry issue. In this book we will review all that the Bible has to say about worry. God is not pleased when we worry. God desires to help us with our worry. God promises to replace worry with joy and peace.

We want you to interact with this workbook. Fill in the blanks; answer the questions; write down some goals; stretch your faith. God will honor your efforts to tackle your worry habit. As we stretch and grow in faith, God responds with love and grace. Attacking our worry habits can develop into a spiritual adventure. We know because God has demonstrated just such love and grace to us as we have tackled worry.

Perhaps you are using this workbook in connection with some pastoral counseling you are receiving. Your counselor may discuss some of these passages of Scripture and some of these principles before you read about them in this book. We hope the combination of the counseling and your interaction with this workbook will make your journey out of worry even more successful.

Enjoy the book. And don't worry about it!

1

Don't Worry about It

Easy to say. Hard to do. Yet we are all guilty of saying those words frequently: "Don't worry about it." That phrase expresses our desire perfectly. We would like to live worry-free lives, or at least have our worry hover at normal levels. But how can we curtail worry? How do we develop a sense of peace about the future to replace the fretting that seems to come so easily and readily our way? We have designed this workbook to help you answer those questions. In this chapter we want to help you address the following issues:

What Is Worry?
When Is Worry Out of Control?
How Do People Worry?
What Do *You* Worry About?
What Does the Bible Say about Worry?

What Is Worry?

Some of the hardest concepts to define are those that are most familiar to us. Worry is one of those baffling problems that is hard to pinpoint. In recent years, though, experts on worry have made headway in defining it. *Worry is a set of negative, uncontrollable concerns that center on some issue with an uncertain outcome—an outcome that the worrier feels will almost certainly be awful.* If you are a good worrier, you might compare your experience of worry with the above definition.

Notice that worry has several important features. (1) Worry deals mainly with the future. Sometimes we feel like we are worrying about the past, but usually in that case we are worried about some future consequence of a past event. (2) Worry is a lonely sport. We worry alone and most people around us do not share the same concern we have about the future. (3) Worry makes us apprehensive and uptight. Worry consumes a great deal of our emotional energy and can leave us exhausted. (4) Worry is hopelessly pessimistic. Actually, worry does not have a lot to commend itself to us. Yet we still engage in worry far more than is good for us.

When Is Worry out of Control?

Because worry is such a private matter, most of us do not know how our own pattern of worry compares with the worrying other people do. One way of finding out is to take the Penn State Worry Questionnaire (see Table 1.1). After you have scored the test, you will have a good idea about how your worry compares with the worry of others. The test can be affected by your current situation. However, your score can still be a useful measure to tell you where you are at this moment in the worry department.

Table 1.1
The Penn State Worry Questionnaire

Enter one of these five numbers to describe how typical each of the 16 statements is of you: 1. Not at all typical. 2. Not very typical. 3. Somewhat typical. 4. Very typical. 5. Extremely typical.

_____*3*___ 1. If I don't have enough time in a day to fulfill my obligations, I worry about it.

_____*5*___ 2. My worries overwhelm me.

_____*5*___ 3. I tend to worry about things.

_____*5*___ 4. There are a lot of situations that make me worry.

_____*5*___ 5. I know I shouldn't worry so much, but I just can't help myself.

_____*5*___ 6. When I'm under pressure, I worry a lot.

_____*5*___ 7. I'm always worrying about something.

_____*5*___ 8. I find it difficult to dismiss worrisome thoughts.

_____*3*___ 9. As soon as I finish one task, I start to worry about all the other things I still have to do.

_____*3*___ 10. I worry about everything.

_____*5*___ 11. After I've done all I can do to take care of a problem or concern, I still worry about it.

_____*3*___ 12. I've been a worrier all my life.

_____*5*___ 13. I'm definitely aware of how much time I spend worrying about things.

_____*5*___ 14. Once I start worrying about something, I can't stop.

_____*5*___ 15. I worry all the time.

_____*3*___ 16. I worry about projects until they are completed.

_____*70*___ **TOTAL NUMBER OF POINTS**

If your total score is 34 or less, you worry less than the average person worries. If you scored 35–61 you have average levels of worry in your life but could still benefit by reducing the amount of time you spend worrying. If you scored 62–80 your worry levels are high and you should start working at conquering the habit immediately.

Worry exceeds acceptable limits when you spend large amounts of time fretting about the future. An indication of worry that is spinning out of control is when you delay taking needed actions because you are not finished worrying about some upcoming event! Worry is out of control when your friends and family start pointing out your excessive worry. Worry is out of control when you are unable to enjoy the peace and joy that God wants you to experience in your Christian life. Worry is out of control when you get so weary of worrying that even you know the time has come to regain control over your fretting.

How Do People Worry?

Worriers come in all shapes and sizes. And so do their worries. You may be surprised how your worry patterns compare to those of other people, both in how you worry and what you worry about. Worry occurs in all cultures and among all types of people. Worry has existed during the entire history of the human race, so we should not be surprised to find that people worry in somewhat predictable ways. The worry cycle typically contains four components. We will look at them one at a time.

===

Remember:
Today is the tomorrow
you worried about yesterday.
Is today really as awful as
you thought tomorrow would be
yesterday?

===

1. Worriers possess high levels of sensitivity toward future threatening events. If the future contains an event or happening that could be a suitable object for worry, the good worrier will have identified it early on. Worriers seem to notice future contingencies that most other people ignore. Worriers often have a keen ability to identify such

targets for worry and always keep a good supply of them in mind. If worriers are not focused on one worry, they always have an ample number of other worries that can occupy their minds.

2. After the worrier has identified a suitable subject for worry, the next step is to pinpoint all the uncertainties and ambiguities of that situation. For example, suppose a worrier named Wally realizes that the annual harvest party for the adult Sunday school class is coming up in just four weeks. Wally begins to think and fret about the party. This year marks the fourth time the class has scheduled just such a party, and Worrying Wally has fretted about the event in each of those four years. Wally never knows what silly games the planners will use this year. Perhaps they will want everyone to dunk for apples. Wally hates that wet, cold game. And then he never knows ahead of time if they will call on him to pray before they serve refreshments. Will his best friend also attend or will Wally have to pursue small talk with a stranger? Wally knows that his wife is certain she wants to go to the party again this year. He can think of no way to avoid going. He can only think about all the uncertainties and unpredictable parts of the evening. Oh how Wally hates to anticipate these parties.

Notice that in both of these first two steps in the worry process, the worrier is not having to face anything unusual. All of us have potentially threatening events in our futures. And those events contain many unknowns, factors that we cannot control or predict. Most people are not bothered by either of these facets of life. Worriers, however, can be consumed by threat and uncertainty, spending inordinate amounts of time lost in thought and worry regarding them.

3. For each of these uncertainties, worriers anticipate the most negative of outcomes. Wally does not think just about dunking for apples, he thinks about making a fool of himself in the game. Maybe everyone will laugh at him.

Maybe he will be the very worst performer of the evening. Maybe his clothes will get soaked, and he will have to spend the rest of the evening miserably wet. Maybe they will ask him to pray and he will stumble over his words. Maybe no one will want to chitchat with him and he will have to sit on the edge of the party in isolation. Wally, and all typical worriers, tend to focus on the most negative of outcomes to these threatening and ambiguous parts of the future.

4. Finally, the worry cycle is complete when worriers get trapped in a seemingly endless loop of asking themselves "What if . . . ?" questions. What if I make a fool of myself? What if I have no one to talk to? What if I get embarrassed again by having to pray in public when I am not prepared? What if . . . ? What if . . . ?

To a certain extent all of us engage in these four steps at times as we anticipate the future. Worriers, however, spend unusual amounts of time on a frequent basis engaged in these bothersome thoughts. We have artificially separated the four steps here just so we can see them more clearly. In actuality, the worrier just worries and is seldom aware of all the steps involved in the process.

So how do people worry? They possess an uncanny ability to know what is potentially threatening in the future. They are proficient in spotting all the uncertainties and ambiguities of those future events. They then attach the most negative of outcomes to these uncertainties, and get trapped in an endless cycle of "What if . . . ?" questions.

What Do *You* Worry About?

When all is said and done, the worry patterns of other people are not as important as your own. You are the one who is trying to replace worry with God's peace. We need now to understand your patterns as we develop a strategy of attack. One way of learning how you worry is to take the Worry Inventory (Table 1.2). This list of 20 worries is only suggestive, but the table may help you identify the many concerns that occupy your worry time.

Table 1.2
Worry Inventory

Never **R**arely **S**ometimes **O**ften **A**lways
I worry that:

_____ 1. I'll lose my home.
_____ 2. I'll run out of money.
_____ 3. I won't be able to be independent.
_____ 4. I won't have money to give my children.
_____ 5. I'll lose my job.
_____ 6. I'll lose my mind.
_____ 7. I won't be able to get around.
_____ 8. Strangers will have to take care of me.
_____ 9. I'll go bankrupt.
_____10. I'll have a serious accident.
_____11. I'll have a terminal diagnosis.
_____12. Those close to me will die.
_____13. My children will turn out poorly.
_____14. No one will want to be around me.
_____15. I will be robbed or mugged.
_____16. I'll lose my family.
_____17. I won't be able to visit friends.
_____18. My friends or family members will die.
_____19. I'll get depressed.
_____20. I'll be all alone.

You may discover that much of your worry pattern centers on health concerns. Facing an uncertain future of physical health is difficult for many people, but some of us worry more about declining health than others do. You may find that most of your concerns are financial in nature. Issues of income and security are also very common. Vacillating economic conditions can make these worries wax and wane. Social issues such as possible embarrassment or shame can be crippling worries for some people. These worriers can be continually threatened by social obligations for fear the occasion will bring humiliation or embarrassment. Finally, many people worry a great deal about work or school. How will my employer/professor evaluate my performance? Will my work be good enough to meet needed standards?

Now that we know a little about what worry is, how much worry is too much, how worry works, and how you worry, we need to explore what the Bible has to say about worry. We will find that Scripture has a great deal to teach us about this troubling human condition.

What Does the Bible Say about Worry?

Let's face it, all of us live every day of our lives by faith. By faith you drive your car, trusting your very existence to a couple of rubber hoses filled with brake fluid. Every time you eat out, you do so by faith in the cook and the waiter. When you climb aboard an airplane, you place your faith in a whole host of engineers, maintenance personnel, the control tower, and flight crew. Every time you turn on the faucet to get a drink of water, you do so by faith. You trust your health to a filter system that you've never seen! Faith is not an optional activity for twentieth-century people. The only real option is the object of our faith, and it is the object of our faith that determines whether or not we will struggle with worry.

You may be wondering why we're talking about faith in a book that's supposed to be about worry. We include in this first chapter a discussion of faith because faith is the exact opposite of worry. Most of us don't worry about the tap water because we have learned through past experience that it's *OK* to drink. We never give a second thought to applying pressure to the brake pedal because it has always stopped us in the past. There is simply no good reason to believe that it won't stop us again. The point is we *learn* to live by faith. Learning to live by faith is the first biblical step toward eliminating worry from our lives.

Faith is so crucial to our spirits that Hebrews 11:6 identified it as an absolute if we hope to please God. "*And without faith it is impossible to please God, because anyone who comes to him must believe that he exists and that he rewards those who earnestly seek him.*" Faith is the oil in the machinery of life, worry is the sand. A little sand can go a long way toward destroying expensive equipment. Likewise, a little worry can grind away at your confidence for living and leave you paralyzed.

Faith is not some magical whammy that comes upon us suddenly. Faith is learned. The first step of that learning process is to admit to ourselves that we really do live every day by faith. Once that is understood, it's not far to the next step of realizing that, if you are willing to trust a waiter or pilot that you don't know and who is capable of making a mistake, why not learn to trust the God you do know who never makes an error? Having admitted that faith in God is necessary, then we need to turn to the source of faith building. Clearly, the best source for personal faith enhancement is the Bible. Romans 10:17 states, "Consequently, faith comes from hearing the message, and the message is heard through the word of Christ." The word of Christ is the Bible. As you begin to read and internalize Scripture, faith in the author begins to grow. Since faith is the exact opposite of worry, worry will begin to evaporate.

Understanding the role of faith is the positive side of the equation. Identifying worry for what it really is, is the other. Like it or not, worry is wrong. Unless one is willing to admit this, justification and rationalization will continue to grant worry a foothold in your heart. Jesus said, "Therefore do not worry about tomorrow, for tomorrow will worry about itself. Each day has enough trouble of its own" (Matt. 6:34).

The phrase *"Do not worry"* is not a divine suggestion. Jesus was not sheepishly implying that "worry was a bad idea." He gave a direct emphatic command that, when violated, equals sin. Jesus labeled worry for what it is: sin. He stated that his followers were not to worry about tomorrow and suggested an alternative. The alternative was to let tomorrow worry about tomorrow. As ironic as it may sound, Jesus was forcing his followers to focus upon today. He wasn't willing to concede even the slightest concession in the arena of worry about the future. Since human beings don't worry about the past, Jesus didn't leave us much about which to worry! Some may argue that they worry about the past, but the truth is, they are worrying about the future ramifications of the past, which is off limits by divine decree.

There are several reasons why Jesus said what he did about worry. First of all, worry accuses God of being a liar. God has promised to meet all of your needs (Phil. 4:19). Needs are one of the things we worry about. Worry blatantly disagrees and argues that God is either unable or unwilling to fulfill his promise. Second, worry questions the sovereignty of God. He has promised to use everything that comes into our lives for good (Rom. 8:28). God is never caught by surprise. Worry finds a thousand reasons why God's promise can't possibly be true under the current circumstances. Further, worry questions the sincerity of God. God has promised that he will never abandon you. In Hebrews 13:5–6 God states, "Never will I leave you; never will I forsake you." Worry erodes away our faith and causes us to wonder if God will really be there when we need him. Apparently, the confidence of God's presence was enough for the writer of Hebrews, since he went on to say, "So we say with confidence, 'The Lord is my helper; I will not be afraid. What can man do to me?'"

Worry denies and ignores all of these promises. It plays the "yeah-but" game: "Yeah, but what if the doctor finds something wrong?" "Yeah, but you don't know my husband." "Yeah, but there are times when the Lord hasn't come through for me the way he should." The "yeah-buts" of life are endless. The problem is, worry knows them all and enjoys playing the game. The "yeah-buts" of worry force your eyes off of God and onto something that might or might not happen. Suddenly, you are living in the world of fantasy and fear. Whether your fears become reality or not is irrelevant to the game. Once the focus is off of God, your potential problems (underscore the word "potential") will loom larger than life.

Finally, worry questions the personal nature of God. The prophet Isaiah offered some wonderful words of reassurance: "So do not fear, for I am with you; do not be dismayed, for I am your God. I will strengthen you and help you; I will uphold you with my righteous right hand" (Isa. 41:10). Worry is unwilling to admit that the God of the universe cares enough to make those words a reality for you. The verse contains some very direct commands and equally direct promises. It charges us, *"Do not fear."* Worry is little more than fear. It is the fear of what *might* happen. It is also the fear of what *might not* happen. God had a very logical reason for his command, he said, *"For I am with you."* Can you think of a better reason to lay aside fear? If the eternal God, creator of the universe, sustainer of all life, omnipotent, omniscient, and omnipresent says, "I'm with you," then why are you worried? Would God lie to you? When worry begins to play the "yeah-but" game, your best response is "yeah-but, God is with me."

It also says, *"Do not be dismayed."* The word dismayed is *sha'ah.* It is a primary root that means "to gaze." It was used to describe one who looked in amazement or bewilderment. It carried the idea of being paralyzed, unsure of any course of action. It is a feeling of helplessness. It is how you feel when your world is out of control. God says that we need not be dismayed because *"I am your God."* Here the promise offered to us rests squarely upon his personal relationship with us. As *your* God, he is on call every moment of every day. He never takes a nap, he never goes on vacation.

Following the two commands, God made three very practical promises. First, "*I will strengthen you*." The word for strengthen is *amats*. It means "to be alert" or "to be fortified with courage." Putting those thoughts together means that God will enable you to be alert to your circumstances and grant the courage necessary to cope with them. Second, God promised to "*help you*." The word used for help was *azar*. It's root meant "to surround." The concept is simply beautiful. Picture yourself surrounded by the loving hands of the Almighty God. That gives you protection on all sides. Nothing can touch you without his knowledge and his permission. Finally, God offered these words: "*I will uphold you*." The word translated "*uphold*" means to "sustain." That's a great conclusion to a fabulous promise. It was God's way of saying he will sustain, surround, and strengthen you for as long as necessary!

Faith Builder

During the next seven days we'd like to give your faith a boost. Since faith is strengthened by listening to the word of God, we'd like for you to spend a few minutes each day reading some passages of Scripture that focus upon faith. Generally the quickest way to get to the basic application of a passage is to ask yourself five simple questions. Answering these questions will take you well beyond the words of the passage and into it's practical application for you today. As you read through the biblical text with these questions in mind, you'll soon personally discover the transforming power of the Scriptures. The questions are as follows:

1. Is there a sin to confess?
2. Is there a promise to claim?
3. Is there an action to avoid?

4. Is there a command to obey?
5. Is there an example to follow?

While you won't find an answer to every question in every passage, you will find that looking for the answers to those questions will take you to the core principles contained within the text. Carefully read through the following passages. Look for answers to the questions listed above and jot down your findings in the space provided below.

Day 1
Jesus' Advice on Worry
Matthew 6:24–34

_____

_____

_____

_____

_____

_____

Day 2
The Faith of the Centurion
Matthew 8:5–17

_____

_____

_____

_____

_____

_____

_____

Day 3
The Parable of the Sower
Matthew 13:1–9, 18–22

_____

_____

_____

_____

_____

_____

_____

Day 4
Jesus Feeds the 5000 and Walks on the Water
Matthew 14:14–33

_____

_____

_____

_____

_____

_____

Day 5
Healing at the Pool of Bethesda
John 5:1–14

_____

_____

_____

_____

_____

_____

_____

Day 6
Jesus as the Good Shepherd
John 10:1–18

_____

_____

_____

_____

_____

_____

_____

Day 7
Jesus Comforts His Disciples
John 14:1–14

_____

_____

_____

_____

_____

_____

_____

2

The Agony of Worry

The Bible and the Feelings of Worry

Feelings make a lousy foundation for life and living. While feelings can be wonderful, they can also be very crippling. That's because feelings are fickle. They are adversely affected by everything from the humidity to hormones! Feelings aren't bad, but building your life around them is dangerous. God illustrated the shaky role of feelings and, specifically, the feelings associated with worry, in Jeremiah 17. Verses 7–10 state: "But blessed is the man who trusts in the LORD, whose confidence is in him. He will be like a tree planted by the water that sends out its roots by the stream. It does not fear when heat comes; its leaves are always green. It has no worries in a year of drought and never fails to bear fruit." "The heart is deceitful above all things and beyond cure. Who can understand it? I the LORD search the heart and examine the mind, to reward a man according to his conduct, according to what his deeds deserve." These verses contain some very helpful insights about the feelings of worry. Most important, they identify the source of worry and offer some action steps for dealing with them.

The first thing we need to do is define what Jeremiah was talking about when he described the "blessed" person. The word blessed literally meant "to kneel." When blessing God, it was an act of adoration but when applied to people, it meant to receive something from God. A person who was blessed was one who had been the recipient of some divine benefit. In the case of Jeremiah 17, it was the blessing of stability in an unstable world. It was the ability to be worry-free in an environment where there was much to worry about. That worry-free mentality was illustrated in the word translated "man." The root of the word described a "valiant man" or "warrior." The word picture is quite nice: the blessed individual is one who valiantly addresses life. Jeremiah stated that the ability to cultivate such feelings begins with one's focus.

Notice that the worry-free, "blessed" person is one who has a divine focus rather than a focus on feelings. It says, "*blessed is the man who trusts in the Lord.*" The verse describes a person who looked to the Lord rather than the adverse circumstances of life. It also describes those who have refused to turn inward and throw themselves a first class pity party. Rather, it says that their "confidence" was based in the Lord. That's called a focus of faith, and it's vital for worry-free living!

Remember:
Faith is the oil in the machinery of life, worry is the sand.

Further, that kind of confident, faith-filled living grants one the ability to actually live better in lean times. As we experience God's provision during adverse circumstances, we learn to trust him more in the future. Worry begins to diminish and we find that our trust grows. That trust feeds our feelings of stability and further enables us to function during times of difficulty. Jeremiah described it as having *"no fear when the heat comes"* and *"no worries in the year of drought."* That's why those who learn to live worry-free often do better in life than those who are crippled by it. That's also why we must learn to place our confidence in the Lord and cultivate the kind of feelings described by Jeremiah.

What circumstances would you consider real "heat" in your life?

_____

_____

_____

_____

What shortages in your life seem to trouble you the most?

_____

_____

_____

Jeremiah went on to say that blessed individuals have "deep roots," meaning that their resources go well beyond themselves and they know it. That resource is the Lord himself. The net result of all this is the countering of fear and the absence of worry. Worry-free individuals are those who have placed not only their focus upon, but their "confidence" in the Lord. The word confidence means to "find refuge." When your refuge for life is the Lord, you'll find the blessing of worry-free living. While worry-free living may sound impossible, the verse clearly says *"no worries"*— none at all!

> Where do you typically place your "roots"? In what do you feel the most secure? *JESUS*

_____

_____

_____

_____

_____

The problem we must reckon with is within us: our hearts are deceitful and fraudulent. While Christians know that they should have a divine focus, our hearts endeavor to trick us into looking elsewhere for stability. That's why Jeremiah said that our hearts are *"beyond cure."* The word meant feeble or terminal. Left to ourselves our hearts will rob us of peace by filling our emotions with the terminal feelings of fear or hopelessness.

The good news from Jeremiah is that there is hope. He outlined the prescription for dealing with our deceptive hearts. *"I the Lord search the heart and examine the mind."* God promised that he would help us by intimately examining our hearts and minds. He will help us see through the smoke screens of twisted thinking. When our minds deliver a misdirected perspective of circumstances, our feelings turn toxic and our peace disappears. God is capable of setting our feelings straight because he is greater than our deceptive hearts. 1 John 3:19f states it like this: "This then is how we know that we belong to the truth, and how we set our hearts at rest in his presence whenever our hearts condemn us. For God is greater than our hearts . . ." Like Jeremiah, John states that our hearts can be at rest (in the Lord's presence) when our feelings would desire to cripple us. God is able to override them because he is greater. Once again, the determining factor behind the feelings of worry is a faulty focus.

Another passage of Scripture that addresses the feelings of worry is Philippians 4:6–7. "Do not be anxious about anything, but in everything, by prayer and petition, with thanksgiving, present your requests to God. And the peace of God, which transcends all understanding, will guard your hearts and your minds in Christ Jesus." These verses begin with a frighteningly direct command: "*Do not be anxious about anything.*" That doesn't leave much room for theological "yeah-buts." It's a straightforward command. The standing responsibility of a Christian is to be worry-free. Ideally, we are not permitted to worry about even one thing. While that may sound like an impossible standard, it simply represents the goal toward which we should strive. The war with our feelings is often lost because we convince ourselves that there is no hope. God disagrees and so should we. We need simply to accept his grace when we fail, and then continue to strive toward being the worry-free individuals he has commanded us to be. The question is, is that really possible? Yes! God has given us an alternative to the feelings of worry, that alternative is prayer.

While worry is forbidden, prayer is commanded. I've found that prayer is often the first thing Christians talk about and the last thing they do. Paul wasn't kidding when he penned those verses and instructed us to pray. He used four different words to emphasize the importance of prayer. The first word referred to prayer as an act of worship. It had nothing to do with asking for things, and everything to do with an attitude of praise. It was setting your heart straight by focusing upon the Lord's goodness and greatness. When we worship the Lord through our prayers, our *focus* is redirected back toward God—it's rightful place. The second word Paul used for prayer was translated "petition." It referred to what we typically think of when we talk about prayer. The word emphasized the idea of *urgency*, asking for the things we really need. The third word set the *attitude* behind our prayer. The word was translated "thanksgiving," and referred to the grateful language offered to God during our prayers. The final word was translated "requests." Like petition, it meant "to ask." Some believe that it referred more to *intercessory* prayer on behalf of others, whereas "petition" referred to one's personal needs. Without splitting hairs, the meaning is obvious: prayer, all kinds of prayer is the divinely instructed, superior alternative to worry. On the other hand, worry is a human option to prayer.

1 Peter 5:7 instructs: "Cast all your anxiety on him because he cares for you." So how do you cast your feelings of anxiety and worry upon the Lord? The answer is prayer, all kinds of prayer! The word "cast" is in a Greek tense that means to cast it upon him once and for all. Once an issue is tossed his way you need not worry because "*he cares for you.*" The word "cares" is in a tense that means he never stops caring. The application for us is simply wonderful; we can forget about worrying over something because his undying concern won't ever allow him to forget!

Now, look back to the Philippians passage. Philippians 4:7 described the outcome of prayer: "And the peace of God, which transcends all understanding, will guard your hearts and your minds in Christ Jesus." That's an amazing promise. Interestingly, it is not a promise to give us all the things we ask for; rather, it is a promise directed toward our feelings and thoughts! When we pray, God will go to work on our feelings. The promise is that the peace of God will guard our hearts and minds. Our entire emotional makeup can be altered, enhanced, or stabilized by the guarding and keeping power of Jesus Christ. Notice that the one doing the

guarding is Christ himself! The word "guard" was a colorful military term. It described the role of a sentinel on the
wall. His job was to continually scan the horizon for the
enemy; once spotted, the city was alerted to the danger, and
the sentinel became a warrior. In this context, our enemy
is the worry of our hearts. Christ himself has offered to
stand guard over our feelings when we are willing to pray.
He has promised both to alert us (our minds), and to protect our feelings (our hearts).

The final thought from this passage is connected with
the human unreasonableness of the whole concept of
worry. The verse described Jesus' supernatural ability to
protect our feeling process as "*transcending all understanding.*" The process being described here is not some
emotional band-aid or mind-twisting affirmation statements. While it may seem illogical to think that prayer
can really affect how one feels, the fact is, God is in the
business of doing things that are beyond human com-
prehension. He is able to provide peace in the place of
worry, and the avenue through which he has chosen to
do so is prayer.

During the next week we would like you to develop a
prayer journal. As you have already seen, the biblical antidote to the feelings associated with worry is prayer. Most
of us have a difficult time with prayer. It shouldn't be all
that hard to accomplish, but more often that not, something interferes with those priceless moments with our
creator. It's not uncommon to have your mind wander off
on a dozen different rabbit trails, or to find yourself saying
the same thing over and over again. Many people find it
difficult to stay awake and discover that what started out
as well-intended prayers, somehow drifted into dream
land. The best cure for an anemic prayer life is a prayer
journal. During the next few days, take every worry that
comes to your mind and write it below under the heading
of "Request." Then use your prayer journal every day as a

prayer list. When God answers a prayer or removes a worry, write it down on the opposite side of the page. You'll find that your prayer life will stay more focused and you'll be able to identify and celebrate God's work in your life as your prayers are answered.

Prayer Journal

Request	Answer
Nay Safely - mmm JADE	
The Bowing alone	
Health - m, m, m, N & A &	
Me - digging more	
Libro	
dentist	
Fear	
nothing to do	
aye	
Brief	

New Perspectives on Worry

We have seen how our Christian experience is intimately connected with our goal of containing worry. The task before us is one of faith. We must learn how to engage ourselves in significant prayer if we are to conquer the worry habit. Faith and prayer go hand in hand. Both are vital to our efforts to curtail worry.

We have already suggested how to begin your prayer venture. In this section of the chapter we want to add some more items to your prayer list. God will hear the prayer of the worrier who prays, "God, please help me stop worrying." But God will also hear even more specific prayers. We want to give you some very pointed requests that you can make of God as you develop your prayer life. We want to ask God to form some new perspectives in us that will help us to break up the patterns of worry that so easily consume us. As God answers our prayers and gives us new attitudes and viewpoints, we will find ourselves worrying less and enjoying God's peace and joy more.

First we want you to interact with the opinion checklist in Table 2.1. These statements will help you identify some

Table 2.1
Opinion Checklist

The following statements represent opinions people have about worry. Read each of them and put a check mark beside the statements that you agree with, remarks that you might make yourself.

_____ I feel I should work on my worry problem all by myself without the help of others.

_____ God is not concerned about my worry problems. He just wants me to stop it.

__✓____ I can never grow in my Christian life until I get this worry problem under control.

_____ God never leaves me, even when I'm engaged in my worry habit.

__✓____ I think I have worried too many years to be able to enjoy God's peace.

_____ Maybe a group of concerned Christians could help me as I attack my worry problem.

_____ When I worry I am usually uptight.

_____ I find it hard to worry when I am relaxed.

_____ I genuinely need a greater sense of God's peace in my life.

__✓____ I think that conquering my worry habit could be an important part of my spiritual growth.

_____ Faith is primarily what we have to exercise at the time of conversion.

_____ The Bible teaches us to be worried about the future.

__✓____ We have to exercise faith to live the Christian life.

_____ Christians should not think about the future at all.

of the opinions you have regarding the issues we want to discuss next. Once you have checked those items with which you agree, begin working through the seven new perspectives we would like you to pray about. As God answers your prayers you will find the worry problem consuming less and less of your time and energy.

New Perspective No. 1:
Relaxation Can Help Me

Have you ever noticed your frame of mind when you are worrying? As these worrisome thoughts race through your head, do they calm you down or wind you up? Most people experience a great deal of tension and uptightness when they are worrying. Worry does not tend to help us feel better prepared for the future; worry usually just makes us dread the future all the more. Hence we wind up feeling nervous and agitated.

Relaxation represents a part of normal living that many worriers have trouble experiencing. What is relaxation? Relaxation is to awakeness what deep sleep is to sleep. In other words, you can sleep lightly or deeply. You also can be awake and be very hyper and uptight or you can be awake and relaxed. Relaxation is a special, calmed state of being awake.

The field of pop psychology has emphasized relaxation recently as a needed antidote to our modern way of living. No one argues that we live in an uptight world. People run, rush, and storm through life. Many of us act as if we do not know how to relax. Yet we should include more relaxation into our daily pattern of life.

Some Christian authors have objected to this emphasis on relaxation. These critics claim that relaxation belongs to New Age philosophies and has no part to play in the life of the believer. However, our criticisms of relaxation should be reserved for some of the techniques that pop psychol-

ogy authors advocate for achieving relaxation rather than
for relaxation itself. If God grants us some relaxation in answer to our prayers, surely that means of obtaining some
relaxation in our daily living is not wrong.

God is not displeased when we relax. We all intuitively
know what research confirms about worry. We are very
poor worriers when we are relaxed. Thus when God brings
some relaxation our way, our worry patterns will be dis-
rupted and diluted.

New Perspective No. 2:
I Am Not Alone When I Worry

The Bible has a great deal to say about worry. As we are
finding out, the Bible labels worry as sin. When we worry
we are not expressing faith in God's providential and loving care for us. So if we sin when we worry, does that mean
that God abandons us when we worry? Or is God with us
even when we fall prey to the sinful habit of worry?

The answer to this question becomes important when
we try to break up our worry pattern and learn how to enjoy
God's peace in its place. If God abandons me every time I
worry, how can I benefit from the God whom the psalmist
described as "a stronghold in times of trouble" (Ps. 9:9)?

In answer to this question we do know that Jesus left us
with a wonderful promise. "Surely I am with you always,
even to the very end of the age" (Matt. 28:20b). If Jesus is
with us, even in times of great struggle and weakness, then
he can help and aid us. We also know from Scripture that
Jesus is sympathetic with our struggles and can empathize
with us as no other human being can. "For we do not have
a high priest who is unable to sympathize with our weak-
nesses, but we have one who has been tempted in every
way, just as we are—yet without sin" (Heb. 4:15).

Jesus knows how strong the temptation to worry is. He
knows how easily we can fall into the trap of worry

because he faced the very same pressures. Jesus did not sin. So we can conclude that he did not worry in a sinful manner. He showed great concern about the future the night before his death when he cried out to God for help in the Garden of Gethsemane. Yet he did not sin. His very example of praying to God in the time of trouble is an important model for us.

Thought to Ponder:
Worry is like a rocking chair;
it will give you something to do,
but it won't get you anywhere.

We need to realize that God is with us even in the midst of our trouble. Jesus understands the great pressure to give in to the sin of worry that we experience. God's offer to be a help to us is valid even when we worry. We need to ask God to help us realize that we are not alone when we worry.

New Perspective No. 3: Conquering Worry Will Be Part of My Spiritual Growth

All too often we think that we can relate to God only when we are perfect. We know God is displeased with us when we sin. Therefore, we can conclude that he only works in the lives of people who have all of their problems under control. This conclusion is obviously wrong. Countless examples in the Bible show us that God is actively at work in the lives of imperfect people. The apostle Peter is a prime example. In spite of repeated failures, God was shaping him into a mighty force in the church during all those times of struggle and failure.

We do not have to conquer our worry patterns before God will bring spiritual maturity and growth into our lives. We can pray that God will help us conquer worry as part of our spiritual growth. In fact, as I exercise the faith that is needed to conquer worry, and as I engage in the work of prayer to form these new perspectives, I will be gaining spiritual strength and vitality. Attacking my worry patterns can be an encouraging spiritual adventure for me as I allow God to do his sovereign work in my life.

New Perspective No. 4: Faith Is Action

As we have seen earlier in this chapter, faith is an important component of our attack on worry. We must realize, however, that faith is not passivity. Faith is not resignation. Faith is not inactivity. Faith is the active expression of our desire for God to work in and through our lives.

A Tidbit from History

Do you know that the English verb "to worry" has an archaic definition: "to kill a person or animal by compressing the throat; to strangle"? This rather severe definition was the common one for the verb "to worry" from the fourteenth through the eighteenth centuries. Only in the nineteenth century did the verb take on the more familiar meaning "to cause distress of mind; to make anxious and ill at ease" (Oxford Unabridged Dictionary). The archaic meaning of the verb "to worry" ought to remind us that worry can strangle all the joy and peace out of our lives if we let it roam uncontrolled through our minds.

God clearly wants to shape us all into conformity with the image of his son, Jesus Christ (Col. 3:9, 10). God has given us the indwelling Holy Spirit to assist us in our spiritual growth (Gal. 5:22–23). When we sincerely want God to work in our lives we must exercise active faith to incorporate the truths of God's word into our lives. The Holy Spirit will energize us as we step out in faith. But God will never initiate the process for us. God expects us to *exercise* faith, to move directly into the problem of worry in the strength of the Holy Spirit. God honors this kind of faith. Faith that is active and energized by the Spirit.

New Perspective No. 5:
Peace Is the Antidote for Worry

God's good gift to worriers is peace. In fact, peace is an antidote for worry. If we are enjoying God's peace, worry will not consume us. If we are lost in a whirl of worry, our hearts are not going to demonstrate the peace that God wants us to possess. Notice what Paul writes in his letter to the church at Philippi. "Do not be anxious about anything, but in everything, by prayer and petition, with thanksgiving, present your requests to God. And the peace of God, which transcends all understanding, will guard your hearts and your minds in Christ Jesus" (Phil. 4:6–7).

Notice that peace replaces anxiety and worry. Notice also that the Bible instructs us to pray when we are anxious and worried. When God answers those requests that we present to him, we will experience peace that defies understanding. This peace will protect us and our minds in Christ Jesus.

If God grants you this new perspective, that peace is the antidote for worry, your Bible study will take on new life and meaning. When you read the many promises in the Bible regarding peace, you will gain additional ammunition to combat the evil of worry in your life by claiming the peace that God wants you to have in its place.

New Perspective No. 6: The Future Is in God's Hands

We have seen how worriers anticipate the worst about the future. Dread consumes the worrier, especially when the *future* contains elements beyond our personal control. Meanwhile we waste vast amounts of time in the *present* by continually worrying. We allow memories of events in the *past* to distort our views of what is going to happen in the future.

Meanwhile God wants us to have a balanced perspective on the three major kinds of time: the past, the present, and the future. The Bible tells us that we are to remember the past and to learn from it (2 Tim. 2:8). We are not, however, to let the past dominate and tyrannize us. Regarding the present, the Bible commands us to be good and faithful stewards of the time that we do have (Col. 3:23–24) and to let our minds be occupied with positive and helpful thoughts (Phil. 4:8). We are clearly responsible for how we use present time. And regarding the future, the Bible tells us not to worry as do the heathen but to trust the future into God's hands (Matt. 6:25–34).

The believer must keep all three aspects of time in balance. We must view the past, the present, and the future just as God wishes us to view them. The Bible is not at all ambiguous here: we must not worry about the future.

New Perspective No. 7: God's Community Can Help Me Conquer Worry

The final perspective we need to ask God to form in our lives has to do with the help that others can give us. Worry is a very lonely struggle. Those of us who worry excessively tend to wear out the patience of our friends and families. They do not want to continually hear about our worries. In fact, they may have directly said, "If you are going to do so much worrying, don't talk to us about it." So the worrier is often very alone and isolated in this miserable plight.

We can assume at the same time that our struggle out of the problem must also be a lonely one, that if we have gotten ourselves into this pattern, we must struggle alone with God's help to conquer it. Yet worriers need to reconnect with the healing resources of the church, and with godly people who will stand by us as we struggle to form new patterns. Mature Christian believers can pray for and with us, they can encourage us when the path gets hard, and they can share with us the wisdom God has taught them in the past.

Worriers need all the help God wants to provide, and God works through his people to help brothers and sisters who are struggling. Isolation from God's healing community, the church, will not help us. Being connected to the body of Christ will provide us with needed support.

These seven new perspectives form a major prayer list for the worrier. As we implore God to form these new attitudes and perspectives in our lives, worry will begin to decline in it's grip on our lives. Then God's peace will begin to replace the fretting that we have practiced for so long.

3

Worrying about Worry

We can understand worry by looking at its three main components: feelings, thoughts, and behavior. The feelings of worry are many and varied. Worriers report feeling anxious, uptight, nervous, and fearful. We have seen how Scripture instructs us about what to do with those feelings. We are to pray that the God of all peace will take those feelings from us and replace them with a peace that surpasses all human understanding.

In this chapter we want to learn about the thoughts of worry. Later we will look at the behaviors of worry and determine how to replace them with new action. The thoughts of worry are the easiest of these three to understand. After all, worry is a thinking process. We are all aware that a central feature of worry is the pattern of recurring and racing thoughts that preoccupy us with the uncertain and negative possibilities contained in future events.

41

Your Worry Journal

The human thinking process is a marvelous creation of God, and although scientists have studied the human brain for decades, this process remains mysterious. We do know that the brain processes thoughts through a complicated combination of chemical transmitters and electrical impulses. But even though we do not fully understand thinking and how it operates, we do know that thinking is central to human functioning. We also know that thinking is central to the worry process.

Something to Think About: Worry is a small trickle of fear that meanders through the mind until it cuts a channel into which all other thoughts are drained.

A large part of thinking involves silent speech. In essence, we have inner, nonvocalized conversations with ourselves. These private talks are not an indication of mental illness; they are, in fact, healthy ways of planning our daily activities, making decisions, and carrying out our responsibilities. This silent speech process occurs rather automatically and is often just beyond our level of direct awareness. If you think about it, however, you will realize just how much inner speech goes on during the day in your mind.

We also know that our inner speech can be helpful and constructive or it can be harmful and destructive. If we are processing positive thoughts, we have a far greater chance of having a good day than if we are constantly negative and gloomy in our internal speech. The inner speech of worriers is different from the inner speech of nonworriers. Worriers process information differently, and they emphasize different aspects of an event than do nonworriers.

In order to conquer the worry habit, you must learn to monitor your thinking. When you know more about what silently streams through your mind, you will be taking the first step in changing those silent thoughts. How can you monitor your own inner speech? By catching yourself at it. In other words, stop yourself now and then and ask, "What was just going through my mind?" "What was I just thinking?" Normally we do not monitor our inner talk very closely because the process is so automatic.

Once you have noticed your inner thinking patterns, begin paying close attention to this inner speech when you catch yourself worrying. What kinds of thoughts flow through your mind? What are you worrying about? Try to notice how you are worrying, what triggers your worrying pattern, when you find yourself doing the most worrying, and what seems to help you stop the worry process. You will find a series of questions in Table 3.1 that will help you monitor your worry thoughts. Perhaps you will notice items that should be recorded in Table 3.1 during several parts of your week. You may need to come back several times to the Worry Journal in order to complete all the questions.

You will find that the discipline of monitoring your inner speech and writing down the content of your worries will be a step in the healing process that the Holy Spirit will use to break up your worry patterns. The very act of writing worries down helps us gain mastery over them. If you are engaging in some pastoral counseling to help you with your worry problem, take your Worry Journal with you to your sessions. Your counselor will be interested in knowing what you are discovering about your worry. If you are not in any counseling right at this time, share your Worry Journal with a close friend, your spouse, or some other believer who will be interested in what you are learning about your chronic worries.

Table 3.1
Worry Journal

1. I notice that I seem to worry the most when

_____

_____

2. The kinds of thoughts that race through my mind when I am worrying are

_____

_____

_____

_____

3. An exact quotation of one of my worrisome thoughts is

_____

_____

_____

4. I have discovered that worrisome thoughts are least active when

_____

_____

_____

5. The most common worries that I have noticed during the past week are

_____

_____

_____

_____

_____

_____

Typical Misbeliefs

As you learn more about your personal style of worrying, you will encounter several underlying themes that characterize the worries in which you engage. Perhaps the specific content of your worries will vary a little over time. But you will discover that no matter what is the object of your worry, your worry patterns will have some commonalities. Many of these underlying issues are misbeliefs. That is, many of your worries will be based on assumptions that simply are not true. As you identify these misbeliefs you will be able to discard them and replace them with more God-honoring assumptions. First, though, we need to list the common misbeliefs that worriers entertain. See if any of these are common in your worry patterns.

My Worries Are Likely to Happen

This misbelief is very common among worriers. If you sat typical worriers down and asked, "Do you really think your worries will actually happen?" they probably would sheepishly reply, "Well, no, I guess not." But the truth of the matter is that worriers think and worry *as if* their worries actually are going to happen. Thus we call this implicit or underlying assumption a misbelief that we must get rid of. Most of the objects of our worry never come to pass. We tend to worry about things that never or very rarely happen. Meanwhile we have invested massive amounts of time and energy in the most unlikely of outcomes. This misbelief ought to be the first one we discard.

My Worries Are Necessary Because the Very Worst Happens to Me

Worriers are quite sure that terrible things always happen to them. At least they worry *as if* such were true. Again, chronic worriers will sometimes admit that awful things only rarely occur in actuality. But because worriers are always focused on terrible, awful, and rare future possibilities, we can be sure that this misbelief underlies their worry patterns. To expose this misbelief for what it is worth, count up the number of times an awful or horrible circumstance has actually happened in your life. You will likely realize that such outcomes are actually rare, and worrying *as if* they are common in your life is a massive waste of time and effort. We do well to rid ourselves of this second misbelief.

I Need to Worry So I Will Be Prepared for What Happens

Many worriers do not like to be surprised by anything. Thus they try to anticipate every possible eventuality, especially the horrible, negative ones. Thus, their reasoning goes, they will have no surprises. Most worriers hate surprises and try to hedge their bets by making sure nothing takes them off guard. This misbelief is, however, illogical. If you want to be prepared for every eventuality, why don't you focus your thoughts and energies on the positive and good outcomes as well? Why do you focus so intensely on only negative events? Besides, why are surprises so horrible? Why not learn to be pleased when something unexpected happens? We need to replace this misbelief with the sure confidence that the future is in God's hands, and that we cannot control the future by worrying about it.

If I Worry about Something I Can Prevent It from Happening

This misbelief is very childlike. It represents magical thinking that may have started years ago in the worrier's childhood. Surprisingly, these magical thoughts sometimes continue to prevail into our adult years. We cannot prevent something by worrying about it. Remember, God is the one who controls the future; we do not control what is going to happen no matter how hard we try.

Worrying about Something Is Better Than Doing Something about It

This final misbelief represents what happens to us over the years if we cannot control and contain our worry. We fall into the habit of avoiding action simply by spending inordinate amounts of time worrying. We will investigate this misbelief more extensively in the next chapter. Nonetheless, we must diligently work toward removing this misbelief from our inner speech patterns.

Catastrophizing

Worriers are proficient at allowing their worries to spiral into ever-increasing levels of negativity. As you can see from Table 3.2, catastrophizing escalates toward more and more negative outcomes until we are preoccupied with very unlikely and dismal results. Perhaps you will

Table 3.2
Sample Catastrophizing Process

- If I am late for that meeting at work, the boss and everyone else will notice.
- When the boss sees that I am late, she will be upset and will remember the event when she writes my next annual review.
- My review will not go well and I will miss the next pay raise.
- Without the pay raise we will not be able to save money for the new roof that our house badly needs.
- The value of our house will go down so we will not be able to obtain the second mortgage we need to send our son to college.
- If he does not get to go to college, he will have to take a job similar to mine and his life will be ruined.
- Because my son's life will be ruined, I will be a failure at parenting just like I've been a failure at everything else I've ever tried.
- I'm worth nothing!

48

recall engaging in just such catastrophizing. The simplest possibility turns into the most dismal of outcomes. Obviously, catastrophic thinking leads us nowhere and we must learn how to avoid letting ourselves get stuck in this mire of polluted thinking.

A Daily Worry Period

One helpful technique the worrier can use to change worry patterns is to identify a 30-minute period every day that can be completely dedicated to worry. What we want to do is to gather up all the worry that we normally do during waking hours and reserve it for a special 30-minute worry period once a day. Table 3.3 lists some of the most important characteristics of this worry time. Worriers should keep a notepad with them during the day to jot down worries as they arise. Don't spend any time right then worrying about the matter. Postpone all worrying until your afternoon worry period. The notebook list you make during the day will become your agenda for the 30 minutes when you can legitimately worry. Worry as hard as you can. Then pray through your worry list. Ask God if these worries are worth the time they take in your life. Give these worries over to God. Let God be in charge of the future. Let go of your efforts to control it.

Table 3.3
30 Minutes for Worry

- Use an afternoon time slot. Enough time to accumulate some worries, but not too close to bedtime. Worry can interfere with your sleep.
- Do nothing else during the 30 minutes. Try hard to worry as intensely as you can.
- Use the full 30 minutes. If you use less time, your worry may actually worsen.
- Don't stop having your daily worry period until it becomes harder and harder to spend the full 30 minutes worrying. By then you will have broken up your worry habit.

The Bible and the Thoughts of Worry

Feelings of worry are often elusive and unpredictable. They can arrive at your heart's door without much warning. The Scripture we explored in the last chapter identified the source of those feelings and prescribed a biblical defense against them. We are instructed to allow Jesus Christ to stand guard over our hearts by taking our concerns to him in prayer. In this chapter our focus is on the thoughts associated with worry. Our thinking process is the indispensable basis for effectively curtailing worry. When feelings of worry assault us, our minds are capable of determining what to do with those feelings. We can counter them with truth, or our thoughts can enhance them. When our thoughts amplify and intensify the feelings of worry, our thinking has turned toxic.

Worry is thinking turned toxic. Worry is allowing concern to degenerate into poisonous thoughts. It is as if worry cuts a channel in your mind through which all other thoughts are drained. That results in a loss of objectivity and leaves us crippled. Jesus knew just how paralyzing worry could be. He made a fascinating statement in Luke 21:14–15: "But make up your mind not to worry beforehand how you will defend yourselves. For I will give you words and wisdom that none of your adversaries will be able to resist or contradict." Jesus' aggressive statement confronts toxic thinking.

The first portion of this verse is a command, *"but make up your mind not to worry. . . . "* Since God would not ask us to do the impossible, apparently our minds can choose whether we will worry or not. Since we have an option, Jesus said that we should opt for the "not to worry" track. The phrase *"make up"* is a translation of a word that means "to premeditate." Thoughts are a rehearsal for real life. By saying "make up your mind," Jesus laid the groundwork for a rehearsal of thoughts that intentionally exclude worry. We must cultivate a mindset that refuses to entertain thoughts of worry. Worry is simply not an option. When the thoughts of worry come our way, we are to expel them. While that may sound impossible, chances are you already do it in many areas of life. For example, when thoughts of stealing something pops into your mind, what do you do? Do you nurse those thoughts, allowing your imagination to run wild? Of course not, by an act of your will you expel them as ridiculous. When lustful thoughts come to mind, believers do not typically dwell on them for long periods of time—we know that to do so would be sin. We set those thoughts aside and get on with life because we know the thoughts are wrong and that nothing good can come from them. Likewise, dwelling upon, cultivating, enhancing, and tolerating thoughts of worry are equally wrong—and equally destructive. That's why Jesus made the outlandish statement "*make up your mind not to worry.*" Worrisome thoughts are a choice!

The second issue of interest in this verse revolves around the promise Jesus made. That promise was the reason why his followers could put aside the thoughts of worry. Verse 15 says, "For I will give you words and wisdom . . . " That's a great promise for a worried group of people. What more could anyone ask for? We don't need to worry about the words we will say tomorrow because he has promised to give us the words we will need. We need not worry about the decisions of tomorrow, for he has promised to give us wisdom. The verse is certainly not advocating laziness or a lack of preparation for the future, but the principle is very clear: God will provide. One contemporary study after another cites public speaking as people's number one fear. Think about it. Jesus took on humanity's number one worry and said, "Don't worry, I'll help you to know what to say." Who among us hasn't wished they could peek into tomorrow so we could make the right decision today? Jesus said, "Don't worry, I'll give you all the wisdom you need when you need it." What more do you want? nothing

Another passage addressing thoughts of worry is Philippians 4:8–9. In the previous chapter we discussed the role of verses six and seven in our worrisome feeling process. Now, in verses eight and nine, God turned from worrisome feelings to worrisome thoughts. Philippians 4:8–9 states: "Finally, brothers, whatever is true, whatever is noble, whatever is right, whatever is pure, whatever is lovely, whatever is admirable—if anything is excellent or praiseworthy—think about such things. Whatever you have learned or received or heard from me, or seen in me—put it into practice. And the God of peace will be with you." Just as prayer will protect your heart from worry (verses 6 and 7), the right focus will guarantee that the God of peace will continue to stand guard over your heart. Sometimes we unknowingly relieve him of duty by flirting with unhealthy, faith-wrenching thoughts. Let us show you what we mean.

First, notice that the responsibility for our thoughts rests with us. It is our obligation to carefully guard our minds. It's interesting that God says he will guard our hearts but we must guard our minds. What does it mean to guard your mind? It means that we are to screen carefully the raw material we put into our system of thought. The old computer saying goes like this: "garbage in, garbage out." It is not only true for computers, it's also true for the human thought process. Our feelings tend to revolve around the focus of our thoughts. Whatever gets our attention ultimately gets us. That's why we get a queasy feeling of falling when we walk up to a cliff and look over the edge, our focus affects our feelings. Likewise, we worry more when we have pumped our minds full of negative information.

In the Philippians passage, Paul suggested an impressive list of things that should fill our minds. At the end of the list he simply said, "*think about such things.*" The word translated "*think*" meant "to take an inventory." One of the prerequisites to winning the war with worry is to take an inventory of the things we put into our minds. What would taking such an inventory reveal about your thoughts? What kind of information are you feeding into your thought process? Would it measure up to the standard set in verse eight? Probably not for many of us—but if you're struggling with worry, you simply can't compromise at this point. To do so is to feed the monster you are trying to kill!

Paul said our minds should be directed toward the things that are "*true*," and "*noble*." The word "noble" meant things that were straightforward and honorable. Paul said our minds should rest upon things that are "*right*." The word meant that which is "innocent or holy." He continued with the word "*pure*." It was a reference to the things that were "modest, morally clean and chaste." He also included the words "*lovely*" and "*admirable*." The word admirable referred to the things that had an "excellent reputation." He continued his directive with the word "*excellent*." It's a translation of a word that was closely tied with manliness and the idea of valor. You might think of it as the classic idea of chivalry. The final word used by Paul was "*praiseworthy*." The word referred to things that made you want to applaud. It was not the kind of courteous applause that we often feel obligated to render in order to be polite. This was the kind of thing that stands you on your feet and drives your hands together in a thunderous standing ovation! That's quite a list. The question is, how does your reading material fair in comparison? How do the movies and videos you watch measure up against Paul's list of "peace producers"?

G.I.G.O. Inventory
(Garbage In Garbage Out)

What were the last three books you read?
What was the theme of each?

1. _____

Theme: _____

2. _____

Theme: _____

3. _____

Theme: _____

How do they compare with Philippians 4:8–9?

_____

_____

_____

What were the last three movies you watched?
What was the theme of each?

1. _____

Theme: _____

2. _____

Theme: _____

3. _____

Theme: _____

How do they compare with Philippians 4:8–9?

_____

_____

_____

How much time do you spend reading the newspaper and watching the news?
(Circle One)

A. Too little—I never know what's going on in the world.

B. Some—I have a fair idea of what's going on in the world.

C. Balanced—I understand the issues of the day but I don't lose any sleep.

D. Too much—Sometimes the world's problems dominate my thinking.

E. Overdose!—I know so much that I often get anxious, or angry.

As noteworthy and complete as Paul's list may be, it's remarkable that the list doesn't contain a hint of evil or things of questionable character. That's because anything less often sets our minds to spinning. Here's what I mean. Consider the housewife who immerses her mind in a racy romance novel about infidelity, then, for some strange reason she begins to worry about her husband's faithfulness. She might also start to worry about their relationship since it doesn't seem to have the passion illustrated in the book. Consider the teenager who watches some slasher film and then begins to worry about being attacked. Just seeing the movie commercials for "Chucky," (a film about a demon-possessed doll) caused our son to worry about his talking doll friend "Corky." Five years later, Corky is still confined to our bedroom because none of the kids wanted him around—just in case! Consider the businessperson who reads of nothing but "doom and gloom" about the economy. He will quite likely find himself worrying at night about the future of his business instead of dreaming about how to creatively take advantage of the current economy. Is it any wonder that we worry when we watch the news twice a day, read the paper, scan the headlines, watch "Rescue 911," and end our day with an unhealthy overdose of CNN Headline News? We pump so much negative reality and media-induced horror into our minds that we begin to worry about our future. It's a wonder that more of us don't snap.

Not only do we have to contend with the bad news in the world, but our own firsthand experiences sometimes confirm our worrisome fears. During a single month, my wife Sonya and I learned that still another close friend's marriage was splitting up. A young mother in our church found out she had cancer. A young family we know was in a terrible car wreck, the teenage son of a friend is into serious rebellion, and one of our daughter's junior high teachers murdered three people during summer vacation! With all the tragic things that occur around us, we are often left worrying, "Am I next?" That's why worriers need to carefully guard and limit the input.

One last verse illustrates the proper focus of our thoughts. Hebrews 12:2 says, "Let us fix our eyes on Jesus, the author and perfecter of our faith . . . " Rather than focusing our thoughts on the worrisome circumstances of this present world, we must fix our thoughts on Jesus. Since he has promised to give us both words and wisdom, then why not look to him when life is uncertain? He is the author and perfecter of our faith. That means that Jesus got our faith going and he will help our faith grow if we will fix our focus on him.

Perspective Improvers

Use the following checklist to identify some things you would like to do during the next three weeks to help combat the tendency toward worry.

_____ Read the biography of some great Christian.

_____ Limit your movie entertainment to "G" and "PG" films.

_____ Purchase some Christian music to play in your car or at home.

_____ Limit your total news input to 20 minutes a day.

_____ Identify three good things that happened somewhere in the world today.

_____ List some good qualities that you would like to affirm in a loved one.

_____ Call and encourage an old friend you haven't spoken to in years.

_____ Write a note of appreciation to your pastor or Sunday school teacher.

_____ Write a thank you note to God and share it
with a friend.

_____ Turn off the TV for a week or two.

_____ Take a drive in the country or go for a nature
walk.

4

Acting on Worry

We have explored the feelings of worry and the thoughts that accompany the worry process. Now we are ready to look at behavior and how it relates to our worry patterns. Some worriers may be surprised that we are dealing with behavior since worry is such a cognitive function. Thinking is important to the worry process, but worry involves much more of our life than just our thought processes. The feelings attached to the worry process as well as the behaviors we are doing or not doing are also vital to our understanding of worry. If we do not attack our worry habit on all three fronts, our success may be short-lived and shallow.

Changing Our Behavior

Change is difficult. In Guatemala many Indian groups made use of worry dolls. Shoppers can still find these six

dolls in colorful Guatemalan marketplaces. The Indian tra-
dition taught that worriers could tell each doll a different
worry before going to sleep. The doll would work on solving the worry while the owner slept. The next day all of your
worries would be gone. Wouldn't change be easy for all of
us if such were the case? But it isn't. All behavior change is
difficult and takes time.

One of the primary reasons for our difficulty in changing
worry behavior is our backgrounds. Much of what we are
today is the cumulative result of our past experience. If we
are outgoing, gregarious people, we have likely learned how
to enjoy social contacts with people, and we probably have
had a significant number of positive experiences along this
line to shape us into extroverts. If we are shy, timid people
we may well have developed this pattern of social caution
as a result of many early encounters with people, some of
which may not have been too positive. Our past shapes our
present; we are products of all that has gone on before us.

Worry and Behavior:
Our main business is not to see
what lies dimly at a distance,
but to do what lies clearly at hand.
—Thomas Carlyle

Many worriers report that a driving force behind many of
their worries involves a fear of social humiliation. When a
worrier pushes a worry to its limit, many times the ultimate
fear has to do with feeling or being inadequate, experiencing
shame, or being humiliated by something we do or say. For
example, many people worry about the annual Christmas
party that the boss insists everyone must attend. People who
do not enjoy holiday cheer that comes in a bottle or who do
not particularly enjoy socializing with work colleagues can

look forward to these annual events as much as one looks forward to a trip to the dentist. But like it or not, most all of us have to handle the annual office Christmas party.

In analyzing why many people dread this social event, we find out that often a fear of doing something that others will laugh at keeps us from looking forward to the party. Social humiliation is painful. No one enjoys feeling humiliated although some people do a good job of pretending that it doesn't matter.

When the fear of social humiliation takes on a large degree of significance in our lives and when it fuels our worries about future events, we can almost be certain that our past contains some painful experiences that still affect us in the present. For example, a young elementary-aged child might have a wetting or soiling accident at school. The image of that day may have been seared into the child's memory by the real or imagined reaction of other children and the teacher to the accident. Children react in many different ways to such an experience. Some may immediately withdraw from people and begin behaving in a very shy manner. In Table 4.1 you will find some questions that will help you explore this matter in your own memory. You may be surprised to see how much these painful events in your past may still be affecting you.

Table 4.1
Jog Your Memory

1. Do you remember feeling embarrassed or ashamed when you were in high school? What happened? _____

_____

_____

_____

_____

_____

2. What about your junior high years? Do you recall some humiliating events, times when you "died" of embarrassment? What happened in those years? _____

_____

_____

_____

_____

3. Jog your memory in the same way regarding elementary school and even kindergarten. Can you recall some embarrassing moments? What were they? _____

_____

_____

_____

_____

4. Do you think these memories had a shaping effect on how your personality developed? Do fears of such events still motivate you to be cautious and perhaps to worry about social situations?_____

_____

_____

_____

_____

_____

5. Find someone with whom you can share these memories. Many times we benefit by verbalizing them and letting other people know how painful these experiences were.

Change comes when we realize that we are no longer children. When we were young we did not have many coping skills to deal with embarrassing or humiliating circumstances. But now we are adults. Should similar events occur, we no longer have to react to these events as we did when we were younger. Now we have far more coping strategies at our disposal. In fact, we can even rehearse in our mind some coping strategies that we could use in the unlikely event that some of these events should ever occur again. We can learn from other adults whom we have observed. Many people possess admirable skills in reacting to a potentially embarrassing circumstance. By no means do we have to maintain fears that might have been age-appropriate when we were children but that have long since become unnecessary for us as adults.

Replacement Behaviors

In rooting out some of the behavior associated with our worry habit, we need to identify clearly what behaviors we will substitute in their place. We will not be very far along if we do not replace the behaviors associated with worry with new, constructive alternatives.

John Bunyan on Worry

In Pilgrim's Progress, Christian and his compatriots storm the large Doubting Castle in order to continue their progress toward the Celestial City. In the process they slay the master of the castle, Giant Despair. Once they have killed the giant they are able to free two imprisoned captives, Mr. Despondency and his daughter Mrs. Much Afraid. (Note how Bunyan connected depression with anxiety/worry in naming these characters.) After their great victory, they held a celebration. Mr. Ready-to-Halt asked Mrs. Much Afraid, the worrier in the story, to dance. Bunyan wrote that she answered the music handsomely. Mrs. Much Afraid's new behavior is yet another example of the value of taking new actions to combat chronic worry.

Action in Place of Inaction

Worry involves us in almost endless loops of thought. Rarely does the worry process prompt us to take action. Inaction is a major feature of the worrier's plight. We need to learn to take constructive steps to lessen the dread of the future. We need to throw off our passivity and take active steps to face the future with more courage and less timidity.

How can we replace inaction with action? We need to watch for opportunities for action while we are engaged with our worries. For example, if we find ourselves worried about poor performance in the future, we should stop worrying and find ways of preparing ourselves better for the upcoming task. If we catch ourselves worrying about some potential humiliation in a future circumstance, we need to learn how to laugh a little at ourselves so the dread of embarrassment does not hold us captive. If we worry extensively about finances, we need to take steps to do some good financial planning and leave the rest to God. If we worry that we will not know what to say in a particular situation, we need to sit down with a pad of paper and write out some possible scripts for ourselves. In other words, we can learn to take action with regard to the things we worry about. When we take these actions, we take the steam right out of our worries.

Good Problem Solving in Place of Poor Problem Solving

Worriers are excellent at part of the problem-solving process, but only a part of it. Worriers are good at defining the problem, identifying options, and exploring possibilities. But they rarely get beyond this data-gathering stage. As you can see from Table 4.2, the second half of the problem-solving method is just as important as the first half. When worriers get stuck in step one or two, they never make any progress toward constructive action regarding the object of their worries. When you are able to pursue the problem-solving method to its final step, you have far less to worry about than when you started.

Table 4.2
Problem-Solving Steps

Step 1	Define the problem
Step 2	List alternative solutions
Step 3	Select the best solutions
Step 4	Implement the best solution

To illustrate the importance of good problem solving, let's return to the illustration of catastrophizing that we used earlier. In this fictitious example, an employee was worried about being late for work. Tardiness is a relatively minor problem when we consider the grand scope of things, but our friend began worrying about it nonetheless. Perhaps he had a habit of being late for important engagements. Soon our friend lost control of the process and his worry began escalating into ever-increasing levels of irrationality.

One way our friend could have intervened in the process early on would have been to implement some better problem-solving skills. Step one for our friend would be to identify the problem. In this case the problem was the possibility that he would be late for an important office appointment. Arriving late on normal days was not too significant a problem, but arriving late tomorrow could have serious consequences. Step two for our friend would be listing possible solutions to the problem. He could ask his wife for help in getting to the meeting on time. He could set the alarm for an earlier time. He could eliminate some obligations from his schedule so the day was less crowded. From this list of options he would select the best one or two things to do regarding his defined problem.

Once he has completed step three, the only remaining task is to implement these chosen solutions. If our friend had invested his time in working through his worry about being late by using this more complete problem-solving method, all those catastrophic thoughts that led him close to despair would have never occurred.

Facing Events in Place of Avoiding Them

Avoidance is another skill that worriers perfect during their long and frustrating worry careers. Instead of walking boldly into future concerns and doing something constructive about them, worriers often stand frozen at the edge of the issue and never move ahead to tackle it. We need the help of the Holy Spirit to face matters of uncertainty with boldness and courage. Very often worriers will discover that they have far more problems caused by worrying than they ever would have facing the dreaded future event directly and boldly.

One Additional New Behavior:

What's the use of worrying?
It never was worth while,
So, pack up your troubles in your old kit-bag,
And smile, smile, smile.
                                        —George Asaf (1880–1951)

Each of these three new behaviors is connected to the others. You cannot do one without doing the other. But as you begin to replace unhelpful behaviors with new ones, you will take yet another step toward unravelling the frustrating worry habit.

As you seek to put into place these new behaviors, why not check them out with friends, spouse, mentors, or your counselor? Share with them what you are trying to do. Let them give you feedback on how you are doing. Their encouragement may help you considerably as you seek to form new habits to combat your worry.

The Bible and the Behavior of Worry

A poster displayed in the conference room of a computer manufacturer showed three large hippopotami standing around with their gigantic mouths wide open. The words on the poster read, "When all is said and done, more is said than done." Much of life is like that—everybody has an idea, but rare are the individuals who put their ideas and concepts into action. While much of what's been said thus far implies action, this chapter is devoted to it. This chapter is the "so-what" to what's been said. "So-what's" are important. Without them, we are like the individual described by James 1:24: "Anyone who listens to the word but does not do what it says is like a man who looks at his face in a mirror and, after looking at himself, goes away and immediately forgets what he looks like."

The pivotal passage for us during the previous two chapters has been Philippians four. In verses six and seven Paul addressed the feelings associated with worry. He claimed that Jesus Christ would stand guard over our feelings if we were willing to take our anxieties to him in prayer. In verse eight, Paul discussed the importance of our thoughts. He promised that the God of peace would continue to be with us, protecting our minds from the worrisome thoughts if we would carefully screen what we place into our minds. In verse nine, Paul described the final step necessary for us to continue to experience the protective power of the God of peace. Paul wrote, "Whatever you have learned or received or heard from me, or seen in me—put it into practice. And the God of peace will be with you." Paul's threefold assault upon worry looks like this:

1. **Feeling worried?** Pray!
2. **Thinking worrisome thoughts?** Perspective! Focus upon good things.
3. **Want lasting victory over worry?** Practice! Practice what you have learned, received, heard, and seen. Paul was saying, "take action."

Paul was an excellent mentor. He had not only taught his followers about the worry-free lifestyle, but he had modeled it too. He referred to what they had "*heard*" from him and "*seen*" in him. Within Paul's lifestyle, they had heard and seen an individual who experienced the absence of worry and the peace of God. They had watched Paul pray, as well as protect his mental input. Now the time had come for the worriers in Philippi to take action.

The third step described by Paul is a crucial one for people who worry. With a couple of strokes of his pen, he wrapped up his thoughts on worry with remarkable insight. He used several different words to describe the action necessary to deliver worry it's final death blow. He said, "*Whatever you have learned. . . .*" The word "*learned*" placed an emphasis on understanding. It went well beyond learning by rote, and into the arena of learning where one understands principles, as well as the precepts. Paul then used the word "*received.*" That word meant to bring something very near. It carried overtones of "seizing something for one's own possession." The application for worriers today is that we own the biblical teachings about worry as our very own. Putting the two words together would refer to one who has grown to truly understand the biblical principles and is ready to apply them personally.

The next step Paul recommended was to "practice" what had been learned and received. The word revolved around the idea of habit. Paul chose this word so that his readers would understand that defeating worry wasn't a one-time event. It's quite likely that habitual worriers will need to practice what they have learned for a lifetime! Although some times will be easier than others, the struggle with worry will always be a threat to one's peace of mind.

When my children were little, I often watched them sit behind the wheel of our car and pretend to drive. They would try to turn the wheel, make motor noises, use the signal lights, and sometimes honk the horn. Despite all the effort and time spent behind the wheel, two things didn't happen. First, they weren't going anywhere since they were living in a world of make-believe. Second, make-believe driving didn't make them good drivers. My oldest is fifteen now—need I say more? I can tell you firsthand that watching a four-year-old Jaime pretend to drive a car is really different than riding with a fifteen-year-old Jaime, and watching the speedometer push 60 mph! You can bet I've been practicing Paul's three-step prescription for worry! My point is this: the time has come for you to get the car out of the mental garage and to put into practice what you have learned. There comes a time when the best of intentions are simply not enough.

The Scriptures have several specific things to say about worry and action. First of all, we must not allow worry to paralyze us. In Luke 21:34 Jesus said, "Be careful, or your hearts will be weighed down with . . . the anxieties of life." The heart that was "weighed down" was one that was so excessively burdened that it was on overload. That person simply could not function. The "anxieties of life" had proven too stressful for the individual to continue to function. The word "anxiety" referred to the toxic thinking that resulted in a disruption of the personality and the mind. Jesus warned that we must not tolerate that kind of inactivity within our lives.

In Matthew 25, Jesus gave the illustration of an individual who was paralyzed by worry. He told the story of a wealthy man who entrusted some of his assets to his servants. The first servant received five talents, the second received two, and the third received one. While the rich man was away, the first two servants went into action and through careful investments were able to double their master's money. When their master returned, he commended them for their action and invited them to share in his happiness. However, the third servant failed to act; he simply buried the cash. When his master asked why he hadn't taken action, he answered, "I was afraid." His fear of failure had paralyzed him, so he "*went out and hid the talents in the ground.*" His master rebuked him severely for failing to take action and confiscated the lazy servant's talent. The application is all too clear: failing to take action displeases the Lord and complicates our lives.

The Scriptures not only tell us to act, but provide us with some excellent guidelines for our action. James 4:13 describes some businessmen who were busy making plans for the future. They were discussing all of their possibilities and trying to plan accordingly. While planning for the future is certainly commendable, living in the future is not. Worriers tend to live in the future. James rebuked them for the endless speculation concerning tomorrow, and corrected their course with the statement, "Why, you do not even know what will happen tomorrow" (James 4:14). When we allow ourselves to worry about the future, we consume priceless time and energy churning over the unknown. Worry is like sitting in a rocking chair, it will give you something to do, but it won't get you anywhere. James' focus was upon today. He was encouraging his readers to quit living in the uncertainty of tomorrow and to take action now!

Essentially, Jesus said the very same thing in Matthew 6:34: "Therefore do not worry about tomorrow, for tomorrow will worry about itself. Each day has enough trouble of its own." While Jesus said that we were not to worry about tomorrow, he stressed the concept of living one day at a time. In addition to living one day at a time, Jesus' words seem to imply that worriers should act upon today's troubles, rather than being immobilized today by worrying about tomorrow. Worrying is the interest we pay on tomorrow's problems, and the interest rate is always too high. That's why Jesus said to let tomorrow worry about itself and do what can be done today. In short: Get moving! The following will show you how.

Anchoring Change to the Scriptures

Nothing has the power to change one's thoughts like the word of God. That's because God's word is more than idle print on the page, it is alive. It has the ability to touch and change us. Hebrews 4:12 states: "For the word of God is living and active. Sharper than any double-edged sword, it penetrates even to dividing soul and spirit, joints and marrow; it judges the thoughts and attitudes of the heart." The word translated "*active*" is the word from which we get the English word "energize." The Bible is able to energize us for change. It has an amazing ability to cut through all the smoke and mirrors that we often throw up in order to protect ourselves from hardcore truth. The Bible is like a mirror directed at the human heart. It has the ability to reveal and impact our attitudes and thoughts. Once the word is within us, it can effect real change!

The Scriptures command us to take every thought captive. Our thoughts are not to spin out of control; rather, we are to captivate them. 2 Corinthians 10:5 states: "We demolish arguments and every pretension that sets itself up against the knowledge of God, and we take captive every thought to make it obedient to Christ." When worry assaults us with all kinds of pretentious arguments, we are to take those arguments and confront them directly with Scripture. Worriers tend to develop thoughts rather than demolish them. We are to capture them and make them obedient to Christ. Since we already know that God forbids worrisome thoughts, the question before us then is how to take such thoughts captive rather than being captivated?

First we need to realize that capturing thoughts is a real possibility. God would not ask you to do the impossible. Since he has commanded us to capture our thoughts, it is certainly possible to do so.

Second, we must understand that God wants to replace our anxiety with joy. Psalm 94:19 says, "When anxiety was great within me, your consolation brought joy to my soul." God is not playing "hide-and-seek" with people. He genuinely wants to provide consolation for the soul, especially when anxiety peaks within our lives!

Third, the secret to captivating our thoughts and making them obedient to Christ rests not with us, but rather with the transforming power of the Scriptures. In Matthew 13 Jesus described what can happen to the transforming power of the word of God. He told the story of a farmer who tossed some seed into a field. Some of the seed fell among thorns and was choked out. When asked to explain the parable, Jesus said that the seed was the word of God and that the weeds represented the worries of life. The weed-infested soil illustrated those who had allowed the worries of the world to choke out the productivity of the word within them.

Unfortunately, we often make a few steps forward, only to have the worries of life come back in full force and strangle out the life-changing potential of the Scriptures. The problem does not rest with the Scriptures, the deficiency is our personal tolerance of the weeds of worry within our lives. Captivating our thoughts and bringing them into the obedience of Christ will only occur when we embrace the Scriptures the same way we have internalized the patterns of worry.

David once wrote, "I have hidden your word in my heart that I might not sin against you." Psalm 119:11. Our task, as believers, is to internalize the Scriptures so they can transform us. As we learn to implant them within our hearts, the weeds of worry will be choked out. A casual reading of the Bible, or flippant, "Oh yeah, I've heard that before," doesn't qualify for hiding the word within your heart, and it certainly won't produce life-change. The word translated "*hide*" meant to not only "hide by covering something over," but to "hoard and protect." The idea was to value something so much that you constantly protected it from theft by hiding or hoarding it. We need to place that kind of premium upon the word of God within our hearts. Once you've embraced this concept you're ready for the action step.

The action step begins with the selection of specific Scriptures that have been meaningful to you. Since worry is the subject, the verses need to relate directly to the issue of worry. Once the verses have been selected, write them out on small cards.

During the next week, carry the cards around with you. Whenever you begin to entertain worrisome thoughts, take a moment and review the verses. Most importantly, memorize the verses. Memorizing them will get the word off the page and into your heart where it can do some good. Think of this as a prescription. Just as the prescription is powerless to heal as long as it remains in the bottle, the word is impotent until it's in the heart—that's why memorization is vital.

Once the verses have been memorized, develop a ritual by which you review those verses several times a day. Connect their review with something routine. Perhaps every morning in the car before the radio goes on. It might be at meal times, while shaving, walking the dog, or just about anything. The point is to make the verses such an essential part of your thought process that reviewing them becomes instinctive. Finally, every time a worrisome thought harasses you, begin to quote the verses one right after another. While you may need to go through them two or three times, the net result will be *"taking every thought captive in obedience to Christ."* Confronting worrisome thoughts with Scripture and repeating the process of review will produce the fruit of peace within your heart and recreate a whole new way of thinking that's healthy rather than toxic.

I cast my worries & fears on Jesus Because HE said I could.

5

The Last Word on Worry

By working through this handbook you have learned new skills that will help you combat worry. We have surveyed the many Scripture passages that address this problem. You have learned that God desires that we not worry, that we enjoy his peace in its place, and that we must do all we can with the Spirit's help to avoid this sinful practice.

When Jesus commands us not to worry, we must take this problem very seriously. To ignore the command of Jesus is to sin. The worry-free life becomes part of the high standard that Jesus set for his followers. The religious experts of that day did not preach such an ethic of the heart and mind. Jewish religious leaders in the first century emphasized external law-keeping. They observed extensive lists of do's and don'ts. Their focus was on behavior.

The teaching of Jesus focused more on the quality of heart and mind he wanted his disciples to observe. Followers of

Jesus are not to worry, not to lust, not to be angry without
just cause, not to be anxious, not to judge, not to envy. This
ethic is far more difficult to follow. We can successfully obey
any ten external commandments more easily than we can
perfectly obey any two of these commands of the heart that
Jesus gave us. The disciple of Jesus has a high standard to
follow. That is why the church celebrates the coming of the
Holy Spirit at Pentecost. Now the disciple of Jesus has the
indwelling Spirit who forms in us these qualities of heart
and mind (fruit). Now it becomes possible for the follower
of Jesus to obey the high standards he set for us because of
the indwelling Spirit's enabling power.

That brings us to another important question: Is it possible for us to live totally worry-free lives? Can the believer
expect never to worry? Can the worrier who has spent
many a year paralyzed by massive quantities of worrisome
thought look forward to a complete obliteration of the
worry process? The answers to these questions may shock
you. No, we cannot live perfect lives because we are not
perfect people. We cannot live the rest of our days without a single thought of worry, anxiety, lust, unjustified
anger, or envy. We fall prone to these human frailties as
we journey through life. No one can claim never to violate
the high standards of heart and mind that Jesus preached.

The good news, however, is that Jesus forgives us. He
reaches out to us in our imperfections and invites us again
and again to cleanse our heart by the confession of sin. He
never rejects us because we are less than perfect. He knows
our frame, and he knows we are prone to wander from the
path he has shown us. And at the same time he continues
to hold out before us the challenge of living up to these high
and important standards. He desires us to keep aiming at
living an anxiety-free, worry-free, lust-free life, as difficult
as that standard might be for us.

When chronic worriers make headway at curbing the
worry process, when worriers are able to contain it and

keep it from taking center stage in their thought lives, God is pleased. God will reward our progress toward Christ-likeness. And Jesus will invite us to continue making headway toward that worry-free goal he has set before us.

Skill Review

Throughout this workbook we have outlined a set of skills that the worrier needs to learn. When these skills are in place, we have a much better chance of seeing our worry contained and under control. When we combine these new skills with the spiritual disciplines of prayer, perspective, and practice, we have a powerful combination that will curtail our worry habit. Table 5.1 will help you review what you have learned in this book. We can summarize these new skills in the following list of five strategies that God can bless in your life if you are faithful in following them.

Short and to the Point

A well-known sports figure once gave his philosophy about worry to a press conference: Ain't no sense worrying about things you got control over, because if you got control over them, ain't no sense worrying. And there ain't no sense worrying about things you got no control over, because if you got no control over them, ain't no sense worrying. What more could we say?

Change Our "What Ifs" to "Even Ifs"

We have seen how the worrier gets trapped in endless questioning: "What if such and such happens?" "What if . . . ?" "What if . . . ?" After many years of creatively

generating these long lists of "What if . . . ?" questions, the
worrier becomes very skilled at this line of reasoning. The
habit can be a very difficult one to break. To the worrier the
questions are important. If these questions are not addressed, then how can we be prepared for the future? So
the internal pressure to continue pursuing answers to these
"What if . . . ?" queries continues.

One important way of altering this destructive pattern is
to reframe the wasteful questions into constructive statements. Instead of *asking* "What if . . . ?" we need to *state*
"Even if . . . !" Thus we take a question that rests upon a
frightened and intimidating assumption and translate it into
a statement that stands on a more courageous and assertive
base. The "What if . . . ?" questions demonstrate that the future scares us, that we feel inadequate for what might happen, and that we feel totally unprepared and vulnerable.
The "Even if . . . !" statements assume we are ready to face
the future, are prepared to trust God for any eventuality,
and are not intimidated by what might happen. We are not
talking about a vapid and mindless Whistling-in-the-Dark
behavior. We are advocating a confident approach to the
future that honors God and that displays confidence in his
sovereign and providential care over our lives.

To illustrate this new skill that all worriers need to ac-
quire, let's return to the example of Worrying Wally. We discussed him earlier when we were trying to understand just
how worry works. He kept asking himself, "What if I have
to dunk for apples? What if I have to pray before they serve
refreshments? What if I have no one to talk to at the party?"
By asking these "What if . . . ?" questions Wally reveals his
hand to us: he dreads going, he is afraid of going, he feels
inadequate and unprepared for the party. Now if we could
convince Worrying Wally to translate these "What if . . . ?"
questions into "Even if . . . !" statements, the entire scene
would change.

Table 5.1
Review Questionnaire

Now that you have worked your way through this handbook, take some time to record what you have learned by interacting with the following set of questions.

1. List some features of worry and how it works. _____

_____

_____

_____

2. What have you learned about Scripture's teaching concerning worry that you never realized before? _____

_____

_____

_____

3. What has been the hardest suggestion in this book to put into place in your own life?_____

_____

_____

_____

4. What goals do you have based on what you now know about worry?

_____

_____

_____

_____

Wally could say to himself, "Even if I have to dunk for apples, I will survive! I could even put a change of clothes into the trunk of my car just in case the dunking really gets wild. Even if I am called on to pray before refreshments, I can spend ten minutes ahead of time on the day of the party thinking a little about how I might lead the group in prayer!

And even if my good friends do not come, I need to get acquainted with some of the newcomers in the class anyway, so I will take a short list of the people I can talk to that night!" Now Worrying Wally is Venturesome Wally. He no longer acts out of timidity and fear; he now moves toward the future assuming God is with him and together they can face the future.

Identify Our Vulnerabilities

We all need to be honest with ourselves. Worriers need to be honest as well. We need to admit that we have struggles with worry and own the problem as adults. Once we have admitted the obvious, we are better prepared to learn just how our particular worry pattern operates. We need to know what types of stress are most likely to push us toward old worry habits. We need to know what issues in family or work life tend to set us off. We need to recognize when we are fatigued and tired so we can guard against the old worry intrusions that take us off guard during those times of vulnerability. We need to watch for times of our greatest weakness. We can review the principles of this workbook, we can reread passages of Scripture, we can recruit our friends to pray for us, and we can increase our prayer focus as we seek to avoid falling into old worry ruts. Following old patterns is easy. Sticking to new habits requires diligence and determination.

Table 5.2
Peace Journal

Earlier in this workbook we asked you to keep a Worry Journal. Now we want you to work on a Peace Journal. Work your way through these questions and then celebrate the changes that God is building into your life.

1. I notice that I seem to sense God's peace the most when

_____

_____

_____

2. The kinds of thoughts that race through my mind when I am enjoying God's peace are

_____

_____

_____

3. An exact quotation of one of my peaceful thoughts is

_____

_____

_____

4. I have discovered that peaceful thoughts are least active in my life when

_____

_____

_____

5. The most common convictions of peace in my life during this past week are:

_____

_____

_____

Monitor Our Thought Life

We have seen how worry can consume our thinking and inner speech patterns. We need to continue our new sensitivity to what is going through our minds. If we do not monitor our inner thought life, worry can creep in and consume us again. You may never before have noticed what occupies your mind when it is on idle. But now that you know how to notice what is happening in your thought life, you must keep up this new awareness. God is pleased with this new skill that you have because we know he wants us to master our thought life and bring it into conformity with his will.

Implement New Coping Strategies

We have discussed many different ways of handling worry. Some of these suggestions may have been more helpful to you than others. Those strategies and coping mechanisms that have proven most helpful to date are those that you should cultivate and continue using. All of us are different. Different interventions help different people. So utilize those principles that have been most helpful to you.

An Old Fable

Death walked toward the city. A man stopped Death and asked, "What are you going to do?" "I'm going to kill ten thousand people," said Death. The man immediately warned as many people in the city as he could. The next day the man again met Death. "You said you were going to kill ten thousand people, but seventy thousand people died yesterday." Death said, "I only killed ten thousand. Worry and fear killed the others."

Remember That Christ Is Our Companion

Worry is not God's ideal for the believer's life. Peace that surpasses all understanding is God's ideal for us. As God heals us from our painful worry patterns, he grants us his peace. Christ is our companion during these struggles. We are not alone. God does not abandon us during times of our weakness and vulnerability. Worry does not disqualify us as disciples of Jesus. But God does gently call us to work toward worry-free living. And as he calls us, he is present with us in our struggles.

The Bible and Some Final Thoughts on Worry

The most comprehensive passage of Scripture on the subject of worry is contained within Matthew 6. While Matthew was the author, the words are from Jesus Christ himself. He was speaking to a vastly different culture than ours; however, worry knows no cultural or economic boundaries. From the Middle East to Manhattan, worry is as common an ailment as the proverbial common cold. No wonder Jesus addressed the subject with such directness.

In Matthew 6:25–26 Jesus said, "Therefore I tell you, do not worry about your life, what you will eat or drink; or about your body, what you will wear. Is not life more important than food, and the body more important than clothes? Look at the birds of the air; they do not sow or reap or store away in barns, and yet your heavenly Father feeds them. Are you not much more valuable than they?" Once again, the Scriptures portray worry as sin. Not only is what Jesus said important, equally crucial is the way he said it. The phrase "*do not worry*" is a present imperative in the original language. It implied that his listeners/readers were already in a state of worry, and that worry must be terminated right now!

Following his condemnation of worry, Jesus identified the three major sources of worry confronting his followers. The first was food and drink. Food was serious business for the ancient people. We certainly have our share of hungry people in America, but as a whole most of us don't really worry about our next meal. The people of Jesus' day often worried (and rightfully so) about tomorrow's food. Sometimes the food just ran out or spoiled! Since there wasn't a grocery store on every corner, they couldn't stop by the local 7-11 on the way to Jericho. While concern over food was certainly a legitimate reason for worry, it was still forbidden by Jesus.

In addition to worrying about food, they had to worry about what they might drink. Israel is a dry land. One could walk for miles without coming across any water. That's why digging a well was often the first thing the ancient Israelites would do when they acquired a piece of land. They didn't have indoor plumbing, water faucets, or spring water imported from France. If they did not plan carefully, they could run out of water and find themselves very thirsty, or something worse. The nonnegotiable nature of food and water serve to make Jesus' point all the more powerful. If they were not to worry about the basic necessities of life, we certainly shouldn't worry either.

Following his command, he gave them a tangible illustration. He suggested that they look to the birds of the air as an example of worry-free living. There are a couple of implications here. First, the birds had to work for their food, it doesn't rain worms! When God commands us *"not to worry"* he is not calling us to a life of personal inactivity or irresponsibility. The principle is that God promised to provide, but he chooses to do so through personal effort. Getting yourself into action, and the faith that God will honor your efforts is a superb alternative to worry. Further, a bird's primary concern is always upon today. They are thoroughly content to live a day at a time. Unlike people, they don't build larger nests or bird barns so they can stockpile food. If they are content to live a day at a time, knowing that their needs will be met, so should we. In addition to that, birds don't tend to overindulge. I've never seen a fat sparrow! They don't overindulge because they have an abundance mentality. They instinctively know that there will be food tomorrow. Jesus' point was obvious. The birds don't sow, reap, or build barns; they find no need to

overindulge because they are daily cared for by God. If God
takes care of the sparrows, certainly he will take care of
you. So what's the worry? none

Said the robin to the sparrow;
I should really like to know,
Why these anxious human beings
rush about and worry so.
Said the sparrow to the robin,
Friend, I think that it must be,
They have no heavenly Father
such as cares for you and me.

Jesus continued, "And why do you worry about clothes?
See how the lilies of the field grow. They do not labor or
spin. Yet I tell you that not even Solomon in all his splendor was dressed like one of these. If that is how God clothes
the grass of the field, which is here today and tomorrow is
thrown into the fire, will he not much more clothe you, O
you of little faith?" (Matt. 6:28–30). With that, Jesus turned
to another worrisome issue: clothing. It was the spring of
the year when Jesus delivered this message and the hillsides were ablaze with red poppies. These poppies were
breathtaking when set against the deep green grass on the
rolling hills. It was upon one of these hillsides that Jesus
delivered his sermon. He spoke of Solomon. Historically,
Solomon was considered the best-dressed king in Israel's
history. Jesus drew upon this common knowledge and com-
pared Solomon's attire with the flowers growing in the fields
around them. He claimed that all of Solomon's splendor
failed to compare with the glory of the flowers. Despite their
beauty, the very same flowers were often pulled up by the
roots and used to start fires for cooking. Jesus was en-
deavoring to point out the abundance of God's provision.

Since God bothers to clothe the hillsides with beautiful flowers, which are here today and kindling tomorrow, why then would he not provide clothing for you?

Remember, Jesus wasn't talking about the kind of person who stands in front of a closet full of clothing and complains that he doesn't have a thing to wear. His listeners didn't have much; they were lucky to have more than one shirt. If something happened to it, it wasn't easily replaced in a day. It was to that kind of individual that he said, "Don't worry." If they were not to worry, certainly we shouldn't either!

In addition to people worrying about food and fashion, Jesus identified a third worrisome subject: health. In verse 27 Jesus said, "Who of you by worrying can add a single hour to his life?" Many people worry about their health. When *Industry Week* questioned America's managers about personal areas of worry, 74 percent of them identified health and fitness as their number one worry. While worry can't add a single hour to your life, worry can certainly take an hour away. The Mayo Clinic claims that 80–85 percent of their case load is illness due to mental stress. Worry is the fuel line for stress. At the beginning of the century, bacteria was considered to be responsible for most disease. Today, mental stress is gaining an ever-increasing share of the responsibility for people getting sick. Consider this, you can never worry yourself to life, but you can certainly worry yourself to death. When you begin to worry, the hypothalamus in the brain sounds an alarm. The motor area of the brain sends a message to your muscles causing them to tense up. Your nervous system bolsters your muscles for readiness and your heart begins to beat faster. The tiny blood vessels in your stomach shut off the blood supply to your digestive system. Your breathing becomes quicker and more shallow. The stomach muscles and intestines may go into spasms causing that nauseating feeling. Your blood pressure increases and red blood cells are pumped in from the spleen. Your sweat glands open and your saliva drys up. Sugar pours into your system from the liver. To top it all off, the adrenalin gland releases adrenalin into the blood to maintain all of the reactions. A doctor from Johns Hopkins said, "We don't know why it is, but worriers die sooner than nonworriers; that is a fact." No wonder Jesus told his followers not to worry about their lives, it simply isn't healthy!

Jesus concluded his advice on worry with these words: "So do not worry, saying, 'What shall we eat?' or 'What shall we drink?' or 'What shall we wear?' For the pagans run after all these things, and your heavenly Father knows that you need them. But seek first his kingdom and his righteousness, and all these things will be given to you as well. Therefore do not worry about tomorrow, for tomorrow will worry about itself. Each day has enough trouble of its own" (Matt. 6:31–34). These verses contain Jesus' second and third prohibition of worry. However, the second and third command are different from the first. You may remember that the first command was in a Greek tense that said, "Stop worrying, right now." The implication was that he was speaking to people who were worriers. Following his command to stop worrying, he identified the three common areas of their worry: food, fashion, and fitness. Then Jesus told them again, "*Do not worry.*" However, the second and third time he used the ingressive aorist that carried the sense of, "Don't start worrying." When one puts the two concepts together, Jesus said, "Stop worrying right now and don't start worrying again."

There were two additional reasons for refusing to worry. First, "the pagans run after all these things." The characteristic that most clearly identifies godless people is their worrisome pursuit of food, fashion, and fitness. They are utterly absorbed with the quest for security. Since we are people of faith, why should we carry on as if we were faithless pagans? Instead, Jesus said we ought to expend our energy upon the pursuit of eternal things. Perhaps the greatest deterrent to worry is the consistent investment of ourselves in the things that have eternal value. That's why Jesus included, "But seek first his kingdom and his righteousness, and all these things will be given to you as well." The relentless pursuit of the kingdom of God and his righteousness counteracts the worrisome spirit within us and guarantees God's provision for our needs. Psalm 34:10 states it like this: "The lions may grow weak and hungry, but those who seek the LORD lack no good thing."

The second reason for Jesus' prohibition of worry was due to our heavenly father's knowledge of our basic needs. God understands. He knows that we require food and clothing. He understands our health concerns. As your heavenly father, he knows and promises to provide! Since he has consistently demonstrated his ability to provide for the sparrow and the hillsides, why would he fail to provide for you?

Believing and trusting in God's ability to meet every need is the ultimate goal of worry-free living. Philippians 4:19 says, "And my God will meet all your needs according to his glorious riches in Christ Jesus." If that's true, why should we worry and fret? That verse is absolutely delightful, as well as remarkable. It identifies the source of our provision as "*God*." It distinguishes the scope of our provision as "*all*," and it depicts the supply of our provision as "according to *his* riches!" I can't think of a single need that isn't covered by that divine promise. However, I can think of some areas of greed that may be excluded. We often confuse "needs" with "greed." When we do, we start to worry. That's why seeking God's kingdom first is so vital. As we focus upon the eternal, the line between greed and need becomes quite clear to us and our hearts can begin to relax.

A Letter from God

If God could write you a personal note about worry, say a
paragraph but no more, what do you think he might like to
say to you?

_____ *Sign. Trust Me yes* _____

_____

_____

_____

_____

_____

_____

Conclusion

Abraham Lincoln was once asked if he thought a civil
war was going to come to the country in the near future.
He replied by telling a story about the Fox River. Lincoln
often had to cross that river on his way to the next session
of the court. When the streams of the area were especially
swollen with heavy rains, Lincoln's travelling companions
began to ask, "How shall we get over the Fox River?"

That night they stayed in a log tavern and met a Methodist
presiding elder who rode his circuit through all kinds of
weather. They asked him about the Fox River. "Oh yes,"
replied the elder, "I know all about the Fox River. I have
crossed it many times and I understand it well. But I have
learned one important rule about the Fox: I never cross that
river till I reach it."

We can all learn a great deal from that attitude. The future
does contain uncertainty and perhaps even danger. But God
does not ask us to live in the future. He expects us to live
in the present and to trust the future to him.

We have known countless people who have conquered their worry habits. God can heal you, and you can change.

One particular friend of ours was continually beset by worry. Nothing escaped his awareness. If anything loomed on the horizon that he could be worried about, our friend found it and worried about it. He was known to all of his friends as a world class-worrier.

One day his wife died. The profound shock of his great loss stunned him. All of a sudden he began to realize how wasteful all his worrying had been. He gained a new vision for what he wanted his future to be. He had squandered large amounts of time on useless worry. Now his wife was gone, and he could do nothing to gain back the time he should have spent enjoying her company. So he determined to change. No longer would he allow himself to let time slip through his fingers in worrisome thought. Now he purposed, with God's help, to move out of his worry patterns and into the peace that God so freely offered him in his time of grief.

We hope that you too have started enjoying a greater portion of God's peace in your life. May the truths of the following benediction of God's peace be a growing reality in your life.

May the God of peace, who through the blood of the eternal covenant brought back from the dead our Lord Jesus, that great Shepherd of the sheep, equip you with everything good for doing his will, and may he work in us what is pleasing to him, through Jesus Christ, to whom be glory for ever and ever. Amen.

Hebrews 13:20–21